# *Victorian Flowers*

# ADDRESS BOOK

A TIMELESS RECORD OF
FLOWERS AND FRIENDS

# *Victorian Flowers*
# Address Book

A timeless record of
flowers and friends

PEONY PRESS

This edition published by Peony Press, an imprint of Anness Publishing Ltd, Hermes House, 88-89 Blackfriars Road, London SE1 8HA; tel. 020 7401 2077; fax 0207633 9499
www.peonypress.com; www.annesspublishing.com



Publisher: Joanna Lorenz
Editorial Manager: Joanne Rippin
Designer: Andrew Heath

ETHICAL TRADING PROGRAMME
Because of our ongoing ecological investment programme, you, as our customer, have the pleasure of knowing that a tree is being cultivated on your behalf to naturally replace the materials used to make the book you are holding. For more information about this scheme, please go to www.annesspublishing.com/tree



A CIP catalogue record for this book is available from the British Library

PUBLISHER'S NOTE
Although the advice and information in this book are believed to be accurate and true at the time of going to press, neither the authors nor the publisher can accept any legal responsibility or liability for any errors or omissions that may be made.

# Important Addresses

*A*

*B*

*C*

*D*

*E*

*F*

*G*

*H*

*I*

*J*

*K*

*L*

*M*

*N*

*O*

*P*

*Q*

*R*

*S*

*T*

*U*

*V*

*W*

*X*

*Y*

*Z*

Name
Address

Telephone

Name
Address

Telephone

Name
Address

Telephone

Name
Address

Telephone

When to the flowers
so beautiful,
The Father gave a name,
Back came a little blue-eyed one,
All timidly it came,
And standing at its Father's feet,
And gazing in His face,
It said in low and
trembling tones,
"Dear God the name
Thou gavest me
Alas! I have forgot."
Kindly the Father
looked Him down,
And said, "Forget-me-not".

ANON

Name
Address

Telephone

Name
Address

Telephone

Name
Address

Telephone

Name
Address

Telephone

Name
Address

Telephone

Name
Address

Telephone

Name

Address

Telephone

Name

Address

Telephone

Name

Address

Telephone

Name

Address

Telephone

Name

Address

Telephone

Name

Address

Telephone

Name

Address

Telephone

Name

Address

Telephone

Name

Address

Telephone

With fine ranuncullus and
jonquil fair
That sweet perfumer of the
evening air
The scabious too so
jocolatley dusk
Should there be seen with
tufts of smelling musk.

FROM *THE WISH*
BY JOHN CLARE (1793-1864)

Name

Address

Telephone

Queen of her sisters is the Wild Rose,
Sprung from the earnest sun and ripe young June;
The year's own darling and the Summer's Queen!
Lustrous as the new throned crescent moon.
Much of that early prophet look she shows,
Mixed with her fair espoused blush which glows,
As if the ethereal fairy blood were seen;
Like a soft evening over sunset snows,
Half twilight violet shade, half crimson sheen.

FROM *THE WILD ROSE AND THE SNOWDROP* BY

GEORGE MEREDITH (1828–1909)

# B

Name
Address

Telephone

Name
Address

Telephone

Name
Address

Telephone

Name
Address

Telephone

Name
Address

Telephone

Name
Address

Telephone

Name
Address

Telephone

Name
Address

Telephone

Then comes the tulip race,
where beauty plays
Her idle freaks: from
family diffused
To family, as flies the
father-dust,
The varied colours run;
and, while they break
On the charmed eye,
th' exulting florist marks
With secret pride the
wonders of his hand.

FROM *THE SEASONS*
BY JAMES THOMSON
(1700-1748)

Name

Address

Telephone

Name

Address

Telephone

Name

Address

Telephone

Name

Address

Telephone

Name

Address

Telephone

*The bud may have a bitter taste,*
*But sweet will be the flower.*

WILLIAM COWPER
(1731-1800)

Name

Address

Telephone

Name

Address

Telephone

Name

Address

Telephone

Name

Address

Telephone

Name

Address

Telephone

Name

Address

Telephone

*Passiflora*

# Passion Flower

*Religious superstition*

When the first European travellers in Brazil found the passion flower growing, they identifed almost every aspect of it with Christ's Passion. In the leaves they saw the spear that pierced His side; in the five anthers His five wounds; in the tendrils the whip that scourged Him; in the central column the upright of the Cross; in the three styles the three nails; and in the threads within the flowers the crown of thorns. Later missionaries believed that the luxuriant growth and the many flowers of the plant represented the conversion of the native peoples to Christianity.

*Primula vulgaris*

# PRIMROSE

*Early youth*

Help us to tell her tales of years gone by,
And this sweet spring, the best beloved and best;
Joy will be flown in its mortality;
Something must stay to tell us of the rest.
Here, thronged with primroses, the steep rock's breast
Glittered at evening like a starry sky;
And in this bush our sparrow built her nest,
Of which I sang one song that will not die.

FROM *A FAREWELL* BY WILLIAM WORDSWORTH (1770-1850)

Name

Address

Telephone

Name

Address

Telephone

*Gather ye rosebuds while ye may,*
*Old Time is still a-flying:*
*And this same flower that smiles today,*
*To-morrow will be dying.*

FROM *TO VIRGINS, TO MAKE MUCH OF TIME*
BY ROBERT HERRICK
(1591-1674)

Name

Address

Telephone

Name

Address

Telephone

Name

Address

Telephone

Name

Address

Telephone

Name

Address

Telephone

Name

Address

Telephone

Name

Address

Telephone

Name

Address

Telephone

# C

Name

Address

Telephone

Name

Address

Telephone

Name

Address

Telephone

Name

Address

Telephone

Name

Address

Telephone

Name

Address

Telephone

Name

Address

Telephone

Name

Address

Telephone

Here's flowers for you;
Hot lavender, mints,
savoury, marjoram;
The marigold, that goes to bed
wi' the sun.

WILLIAM SHAKESPEARE
(1564-1616)

Name

Address

Telephone

Name

Address

Telephone

*Fuchsia*

# FUCHSIA

*Taste*

To eulogize the fuchsia is surely superfluous, for it commends itself at first sight. Simply the oldest species, the *F. coccinea*, has always been a welcome shrub, yet the goodwill of flower lovers toward the same has increased all the more as ever newer and more beautiful sorts were discovered and were created through artificial pollination... Every year we get newer and more beautiful ones, indeed we learn through travellers that the more interesting species are still to be awaited from their homelands.

FROM *DEUTSCHEN MAGAZIN FÜR GARTEN UND BLUMENKUNDE,* 1848, VOL 1.

*Galanthus*

# SNOWDROP

*Hope*

The Snowdrop is the prophet of the flowers;
It lives and dies upon its bed of snows;
And like a thought of spring it comes and goes.
Hanging its head beside our leafless bowers.
The sun's betrothing kiss it never knows,
Nor all the glowing joy of golden showers;
But ever in a placid, pure repose,
More like a spirit with its look serene,
Droops its pale cheek veined thro' with infant green.

FROM *THE WILD ROSE AND THE SNOWDROP* BY

GEORGE MEREDITH (1828-1909)

Name

Address

Telephone

Name

Address

Telephone

Name

Address

Telephone

Name

Address

Telephone

Name

Address

Telephone

Name

Address

Telephone

Name

Address

Telephone

Name

Address

Telephone

Name

Address

Telephone

Name

Address

Telephone

Name

Address

Telephone

Name

Address

Telephone

Lavender's blue, dilly dilly
Lavender's green
When I am king, dilly dilly
You shall be queen.

TRADITIONAL SONG

Oh my Luve's like a red,
red rose
That's newly sprung
in June:
Oh my Luve's like
the melodie
That's sweetly play'd
in tune.

*My Love is Like a Red, Red Rose*
by Robert Burns
(1759-1796)

Name ..................
Address ..................
..................
..................
Telephone ..................

Name ..................
Address ..................
..................
..................
Telephone ..................

Name ..................
Address ..................
..................
..................
Telephone ..................

Name ..................
Address ..................
..................
..................
Telephone ..................

Name ..................
Address ..................
..................
..................
Telephone ..................

Name ..................
Address ..................
..................
..................
Telephone ..................

Name ..................
Address ..................
..................
..................
Telephone ..................

Name ..................
Address ..................
..................
..................
Telephone ..................

Name ..................
Address ..................
..................
..................
Telephone ..................

Name ..................
Address ..................
..................
..................
Telephone ..................

*Solidago*

# GOLDEN ROD

*Precaution*

There were also whole fields full of ferns, now rusty and withering, which in older countries are commonly confined to wet ground. There were very few flowers, even allowing for the lateness of the season. It chanced that I saw no asters in bloom along the road for fifty miles, though they were so abundant then in Massachusetts...and no golden-rods till within twenty miles of Monson, where I saw a three-ribbed one.

FROM *THE MAINE WOODS* BY HENRY DAVID THOREAU (1817-62)

*Syringa*

# LILAC

*Humility*

In the dooryard fronting an old farm-house near the white-wash'd palings,
Stands the lilac-bush tall-growing with heart-shaped leaves of rich green,
With many a pointed blossom rising delicate, with the perfume strong I love,
With every leaf a miracle – and from this bush in the dooryard,
With delicate-color'd blossoms and heart-shaped leaves of rich green,
A sprig with its flower I break.

FROM *MEMORIES OF PRESIDENT LINCOLN* BY WALT WHITMAN (1819-92)

Name ..............................
Address ..............................
..............................
..............................
Telephone ..............................

Name ..............................
Address ..............................
..............................
..............................
Telephone ..............................

Name ..............................
Address ..............................
..............................
..............................
Telephone ..............................

Name ..............................
Address ..............................
..............................
..............................
Telephone ..............................

Name ..............................
Address ..............................
..............................
..............................
Telephone ..............................

Name ..............................
Address ..............................
..............................
..............................
Telephone ..............................

*The rainbow comes and goes,*
*And lovely is the rose.*

FROM *ODE: INTIMATIONS OF IMMORTALITY*
BY WILLIAM WORDSWORTH
(1770-1850)

Name ..............................
Address ..............................
..............................
..............................
Telephone ..............................

Name ..............................
Address ..............................
..............................
..............................
Telephone ..............................

Name ..............................
Address ..............................
..............................
..............................
Telephone ..............................

Name ..............................
Address ..............................
..............................
..............................
Telephone ..............................

Name ..............................
Address ..............................
..............................
..............................
Telephone ..............................

Name

Address

Telephone

Name

Address

Telephone

Name

Address

Telephone

Name

Address

Telephone

Name

Address

Telephone

Name

Address

Telephone

Name

Address

Telephone

Name

Address

Telephone

Name

Address

Telephone

> Beauty, strength,
> youth are
> flowers but fading seen;
> Duty, faith, love, are roots,
> and ever green.
>
> FROM *A FAREWELL TO ARMS*
> BY GEORGE PEEL
> (1558-1597)

Name

Address

Telephone

# CYCLAMEN

*Diffidence*

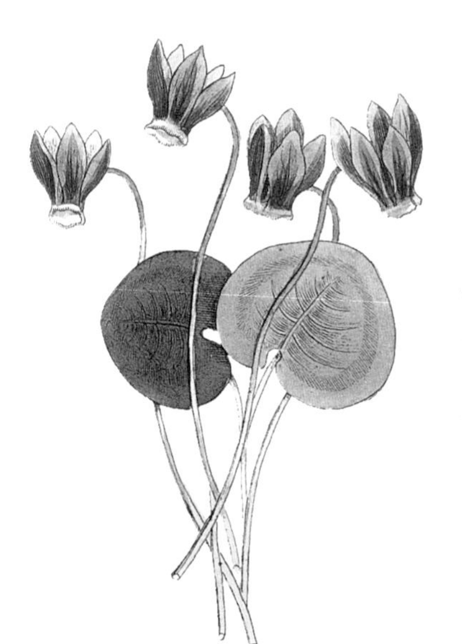

They are terribly white:
There is snow on the ground,
And a moon on the snow at night;
The sky is cut by the winter light;
Yet I, who have all these things in ken,
Am struck to the heart by the chiselled white
Of this handful of cyclamen.

Katharine Bradley (1846-1914) and
Edith Cooper (1862-1913)

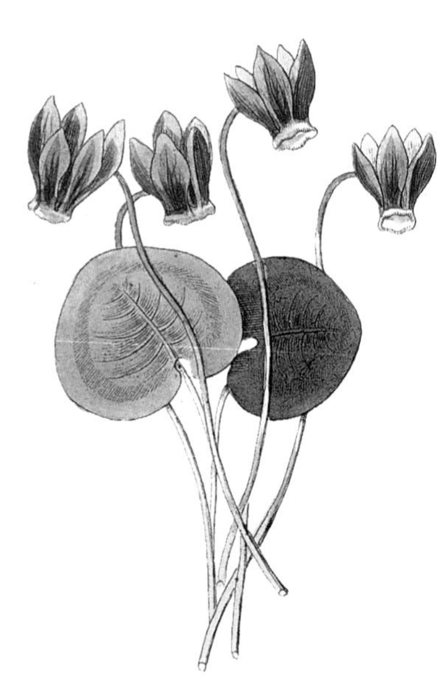

*Dianthus*

# PINK

*Boldness*

Woodley stood among fields; and there was an old-fashioned garden where roses and currant-bushes touched each other, and where the heathery asparagus formed a pretty background to the pinks and gilly-flowers; there was no drive up to the door. We got out at a little gate, and walked up a straight box-edged path.

"My cousin might make a drive, I think," said Miss Pole, who was afraid of ear-ache, and had only her cap on.

"I think it is very pretty," said Miss Matty, with a soft plaintiveness in her voice.

FROM *CRANFORD* BY ELIZABETH GASKELL (1810-65)

Name

Address

Telephone

Name

Address

Telephone

Name

Address

Telephone

Name

Address

Telephone

There fell a silvery-silken
veil of light,
With quietude, and sultriness,
and slumber,
Upon the upturn'd faces
of a thousand
Roses that grew in an
enchanted garden...

FROM *TO HELEN*
BY EDGAR ALLAN POE
(1809-1849)

Name

Address

Telephone

Name

Address

Telephone

Name

Address

Telephone

Name

Address

Telephone

Name

Address

Telephone

Name

Address

Telephone

The red rose cries,
'She is near, she is near;'
And the white rose weeps,
'She is late;'
The larkspur listens,
'I hear, I hear;'
And the lily whispers,
'I wait.'

FROM *MAUD*
BY ALFRED, LORD TENNYSON
(1809-1892)

Name ..........
Address ..........
..........
..........
Telephone ..........

Name ..........
Address ..........
..........
..........
Telephone ..........

Name ..........
Address ..........
..........
..........
Telephone ..........

Name ..........
Address ..........
..........
..........
Telephone ..........

Name ..........
Address ..........
..........
..........
Telephone ..........

Name ..........
Address ..........
..........
..........
Telephone ..........

Name ..........
Address ..........
..........
..........
Telephone ..........

Name ..........
Address ..........
..........
..........
Telephone ..........

Name ..........
Address ..........
..........
..........
Telephone ..........

Name ..........
Address ..........
..........
..........
Telephone ..........

*Paeonia*

# PEONY

*Shame, Bashfulness*

Vulgarity is the idea which had long been associated with the effects of the Paeonia...But there is a race of Paeonias now in cultivation which, for perfection of form and delicacy of colouring, vie with the queen of flowers herself, and many of them are sweet-scented. They embrace all the delicacy of colouring which lies between the pure white, the pale pink, the delicate blush, the brilliant rosy-purple, the crimson, and various other effective and pleasing colours...the flowers are as double and compact as the finest rose, and the blooms of great size.

FROM *THE GARDEN MAGAZINE*, 1874

Peony. According to fable, so called from Paeon, the physician who cured the wounds received by the gods in the Trojan war. The seeds were, at one time, worn round the neck as a charm against the powers of darkness.

> About an Infant's neck hang Paeonie,
> It cures Alcydes cruell maladie.

FROM *BREWER'S DICTIONARY OF PHRASE AND FABLE*, 1870

It was once widely held that a peony plant will last a lifetime provided it is left undisturbed, while uprooting it will bring bad luck. Anyone wishing to remove a peony had therefore to get a dog to dig it up for them in the dead of night.

Name ..........
Address ..........
..........
..........
Telephone ..........

Name ..........
Address ..........
..........
..........
Telephone ..........

Name ..........
Address ..........
..........
..........
Telephone ..........

Name ..........
Address ..........
..........
..........
Telephone ..........

Name ..........
Address ..........
..........
..........
Telephone ..........

Name ..........
Address ..........
..........
..........
Telephone ..........

Name ..........
Address ..........
..........
..........
Telephone ..........

Name ..........
Address ..........
..........
..........
Telephone ..........

To see a World
in a grain of sand,
And Heaven in
a wild flower,
Hold Infinity in the
palm of your hand,
And Eternity
in an hour.

WILLIAM BLAKE
(1757-1827)

Name ..........
Address ..........
..........
..........
Telephone ..........

Name ..........
Address ..........
..........
..........
Telephone ..........

Name

Address

Telephone

Name

Address

Telephone

Name

Address

Telephone

Name

Address

Telephone

Name

Address

Telephone

Name

Address

Telephone

I bring fresh showers for
The thirsting flowers,
From the seas and streams.

PERCY BYSSHE SHELLEY
(1792-1822)

Name

Address

Telephone

Name

Address

Telephone

Name

Address

Telephone

Name

Address

Telephone

I saw the sweetest flower wild nature yields,
A fresh blown musk-Rose. 'Twas the first that threw
Its sweets upon the summer; graceful it grew
As is the wand that queen Titania wields.
And, as I feasted on its fragrancy,
I thought the garden-rose it far excelled.

FROM *TO A FRIEND WHO SENT ME SOME ROSES* BY
JOHN KEATS (1795–1821)

Nobody knows this little Rose
It might a pilgrim be
Did I not take it from the ways
And lift it up to thee.
Only a Bee will miss it –
Only a Butterfly,
Hastening from far journey –
On its breast to lie –
Only a Bird will wonder –
Only a Breeze will sigh –
Ah Little Rose – how easy
For such as thee to die.

EMILY DICKINSON (1830–86)

Name

Address

Telephone

Name

Address

Telephone

*Where the thistle lifts a purple crown*
*Six foot out of the turf,*
*And the harebell shakes on the windy hill –*
*O the breath of the distant surf!*

FROM *DAISY*
BY FRANCIS THOMPSON
(1859-1907)

Name

Address

Telephone

Name

Address

Telephone

Name

Address

Telephone

Name

Address

Telephone

Name

Address

Telephone

Name

Address

Telephone

Name

Address

Telephone

Name

Address

Telephone

Name ..........................................
Address ..........................................
..........................................
..........................................
Telephone ..........................................

Name ..........................................
Address ..........................................
..........................................
..........................................
Telephone ..........................................

Name ..........................................
Address ..........................................
..........................................
..........................................
Telephone ..........................................

Name ..........................................
Address ..........................................
..........................................
..........................................
Telephone ..........................................

Name ..........................................
Address ..........................................
..........................................
..........................................
Telephone ..........................................

Name ..........................................
Address ..........................................
..........................................
..........................................
Telephone ..........................................

Name ..........................................
Address ..........................................
..........................................
..........................................
Telephone ..........................................

Name ..........................................
Address ..........................................
..........................................
..........................................
Telephone ..........................................

The sweetest flower
that blows,
I give you as we part.
For you it is a rose,
For me it is my heart.

FREDERICK PETERSON
(1859-1938)

Name ..........................................
Address ..........................................
..........................................
..........................................
Telephone ..........................................

Name ..........................................
Address ..........................................
..........................................
..........................................
Telephone ..........................................

*Lonicera*

# HONEYSUCKLE

*Generous and devoted affection*

Fair flower, that dost so comely grow,
Hid in this silent, dull retreat,
Untouched thy honied blossoms blow,
Unseen thy little branches greet.
No roving foot shall crush thee here,
No busy hand provoke a tear.

FROM *THE WILD HONEY SUCKLE* BY PHILIP FRENEAU

(1752-1832)

*Magnolia*

# MAGNOLIA

*Love of nature*

In the enclosure the spring flowers are almost too beautiful – a great stretch of foam-like cowslips. As I bend over them, the air is heavy and sweet with their scent, like hay and new milk and the kisses of children, and, further on, a sunlit wonder of chiming daffodils.

Before me two great rhododendron bushes. Against the dark, broad leaves the blossoms rise, flame-like, tremulous in the still air, and the pear rose loving-cup of a magnolia hangs delicately on the grey bough.

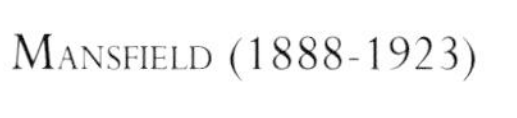

FROM *In the Botanical Garden* BY KATHERINE MANSFIELD (1888-1923)

Name

Address

Telephone

Name

Address

Telephone

Name

Address

Telephone

Name

Address

Telephone

A violet by a mossy stone
Half hidden from the eye!

FROM *SHE DWELT AMONG THE UNTRODDEN WAYS*
BY WILLIAM WORDSWORTH
(1770-1850)

Name

Address

Telephone

Name

Address

Telephone

Name

Address

Telephone

Name

Address

Telephone

Name

Address

Telephone

Name

Address

Telephone

Name

Address

Telephone

Name

Address

Telephone

Name

Address

Telephone

Name

Address

Telephone

Name

Address

Telephone

Name

Address

Telephone

Name

Address

Telephone

Name

Address

Telephone

Name

Address

Telephone

Roses are flow'ring
in Picardy
But there's never
a rose like you!

FROM *ROSES OF PICARDY*
BY FREDERIC EDWARD
WEATHERLY
(1848-1929)

Name

Address

Telephone

*Ranunculus*

# BUTTERCUP

*Ingratitude, Childishness*

The flush of life may well be seen
Thrilling back over hills and valleys;
The cowslip startles its meadows green,
The buttercup catches the sun in its chalice
And there's never a leaf or a blade too mean
To be some happy creature's palace.

FROM *What Is So Rare as a Day in June?* BY
James Russell Lowell (1819-91)

*Rosa*

# ROSE

*Thy smile I aspire to*

Originally, no doubt, when this pretty custom was first instituted, it may have had a sincere and modest import. Each youth and damsel, gathering bouquets of field-flowers, or the sweetest and fairest that grew in their own gardens, all fresh and virgin blossoms, flung them, with true aim, at the one, or few, whom they regarded with a sentiment of shy partiality at least, if not with love. Often, the lover in the Corso may thus have received from his bright mistress, in her father's princely balcony, the first sweet intimation that his passionate glances had not struck against a heart of marble. What more appropriate mode of suggesting her tender secret could a maiden find than by the soft hit of a rosebud against a young man's cheek.

FROM *THE MARBLE FAUN* BY NATHANIEL HAWTHORNE (1804-64)

For the Rose, ho, the Rose!
is the eye of the flowers,
Is the blush of the
meadows that feel
themselves fair,
Is the lightning of beauty that
strikes thro' the bowers,
On pale lovers who sit in the
glow unaware.

TRANSLATED FROM SAPPHO
(SIXTH CENTURY BC)

Name ..........
Address ..........
..........
..........
Telephone ..........

Name ..........
Address ..........
..........
..........
Telephone ..........

Name ..........
Address ..........
..........
..........
Telephone ..........

Name ..........
Address ..........
..........
..........
Telephone ..........

Name ..........
Address ..........
..........
..........
Telephone ..........

Name ..........
Address ..........
..........
..........
Telephone ..........

Name ..........
Address ..........
..........
..........
Telephone ..........

Name ..........
Address ..........
..........
..........
Telephone ..........

Name ..........
Address ..........
..........
..........
Telephone ..........

Name ..........
Address ..........
..........
..........
Telephone ..........

Name ..................
Address ..................
..................
..................
Telephone ..................

Name ..................
Address ..................
..................
..................
Telephone ..................

Name ..................
Address ..................
..................
..................
Telephone ..................

Rosy is the West,
Rosy is the South,
Roses are her cheeks,
And a rose her mouth.

FROM *MAUD*
BY ALFRED, LORD TENNYSON
(1809-1892)

Name ..................
Address ..................
..................
..................
Telephone ..................

Name ..................
Address ..................
..................
..................
Telephone ..................

Name ..................
Address ..................
..................
..................
Telephone ..................

Name ..................
Address ..................
..................
..................
Telephone ..................

Name ..................
Address ..................
..................
..................
Telephone ..................

Name ..................
Address ..................
..................
..................
Telephone ..................

Name ..................
Address ..................
..................
..................
Telephone ..................

*Helianthus*

# SUNFLOWER

*Haughtiness*

Stately stand the sunflowers, glowing down the garden-side,
Ranged in royal rank arow along the warm grey wall,
Whence their deep disks burn at rich midnoon afire with pride,
Even as though their beams indeed were sunbeams, and the tall
Sceptral stems bore stars whose reign endures, not flowers that fall.
Lowlier laughs and basks the kindlier flower of homelier fame,
Held by love the sweeter that it blooms in Shakespeare's name,
Fragrant yet as though his hand had touched and made it thrill,
Like the whole world's heart, with warm new life and gladdening flame.
Fair befall the fairgreen close that lies below the mill!

FROM *THE MILL GARDEN* BY ALGERNON SWINBURNE (1837-1909)

*Hyacinthoides*

## BLUEBELL

*Constancy*

Sacred watcher, wave thy bells!
Fair hill flower and woodland Child!
Dear to me in deep green dells —
Dearest on the mountains wild —
Bluebell, even as all divine

I have seen my darling shine —
Bluebell, even as wan and frail
I have seen my darling ail —
Thou hast found a voice for me —
As soothing words are breathed by thee.

Emily Brontë (1818-48)

Name
Address

Telephone

Name
Address

Telephone

Then will I raise aloft the milk-white rose,
For whose sweet smell the air shall be perfumed.

WILLIAM SHAKESPEARE
(1564-1616)

Name
Address

Telephone

Name
Address

Telephone

Name
Address

Telephone

Name
Address

Telephone

Name
Address

Telephone

Name
Address

Telephone

Name
Address

Telephone

Name
Address

Telephone

Name
Address

Telephone

Name
Address

Telephone

Name
Address

Telephone

Name
Address

Telephone

Name
Address

Telephone

Name
Address

Telephone

Name
Address

Telephone

Name
Address

Telephone

Name
Address

Telephone

Name
Address

Telephone

Where shall I find a
white rose blowing ? –
Out in the garden where
all sweets be.

FROM *WHERE SHALL I FIND A WHITE ROSE?*
BY CHRISTINA ROSSETTI
(1830-1894)

Name
Address

Telephone

I smelt and prays'd the fragrant rose,
Blushing, thus answer'd she:
The praise you gave,
The scent I have,
Does not belong to mee;
This harmless odour, none
But only God indeed does owne;
To be his keepers, my poor leaves he chose;
And thus reply'd the rose.

FROM *TRIVIAL POEMS AND TRIOLETS* (1651)

BY PATRICK CAREY

A romantic Mogul legend from India describes how the essential oil of roses was discovered. Recently married, the Emperor Jehangir and his bride were walking in the beautiful gardens surrounding their palace, where the long pools of water had been filled with roses to celebrate their wedding. As they stood to savour the perfumed air, they noticed that the heat of the sun on the petals had produced a film of oil that floated on the surface. So wonderful was the scent of the oil that they ordered it to be bottled and this attar was ever after the scent of the emperors.

Name ....................
Address ....................
....................
....................
Telephone ....................

*Your ghost will walk...*
*In an English lane,*
*By a cornfield-side*
*a-flutter with poppies.*

FROM *DE GUSTIBUS*
BY ROBERT BROWNING
(1812-1889)

Name ....................
Address ....................
....................
....................
Telephone ....................

Name ....................
Address ....................
....................
....................
Telephone ....................

Name ....................
Address ....................
....................
....................
Telephone ....................

Name ....................
Address ....................
....................
....................
Telephone ....................

Name ....................
Address ....................
....................
....................
Telephone ....................

Name ....................
Address ....................
....................
....................
Telephone ....................

Name ....................
Address ....................
....................
....................
Telephone ....................

Name ....................
Address ....................
....................
....................
Telephone ....................

Name ....................
Address ....................
....................
....................
Telephone ....................

Name
Address

Telephone

Name
Address

Telephone

Name
Address

Telephone

Name
Address

Telephone

Name
Address

Telephone

Name
Address

Telephone

Name
Address

Telephone

Name
Address

Telephone

Each Morn a thousand
Roses brings.

FROM THE *RUBAIYAT OF*
*OMAR KHAYYAM*
TRANS.
EDWARD FITZGERALD
(1809-1883)

Name
Address

Telephone

Name
Address

Telephone

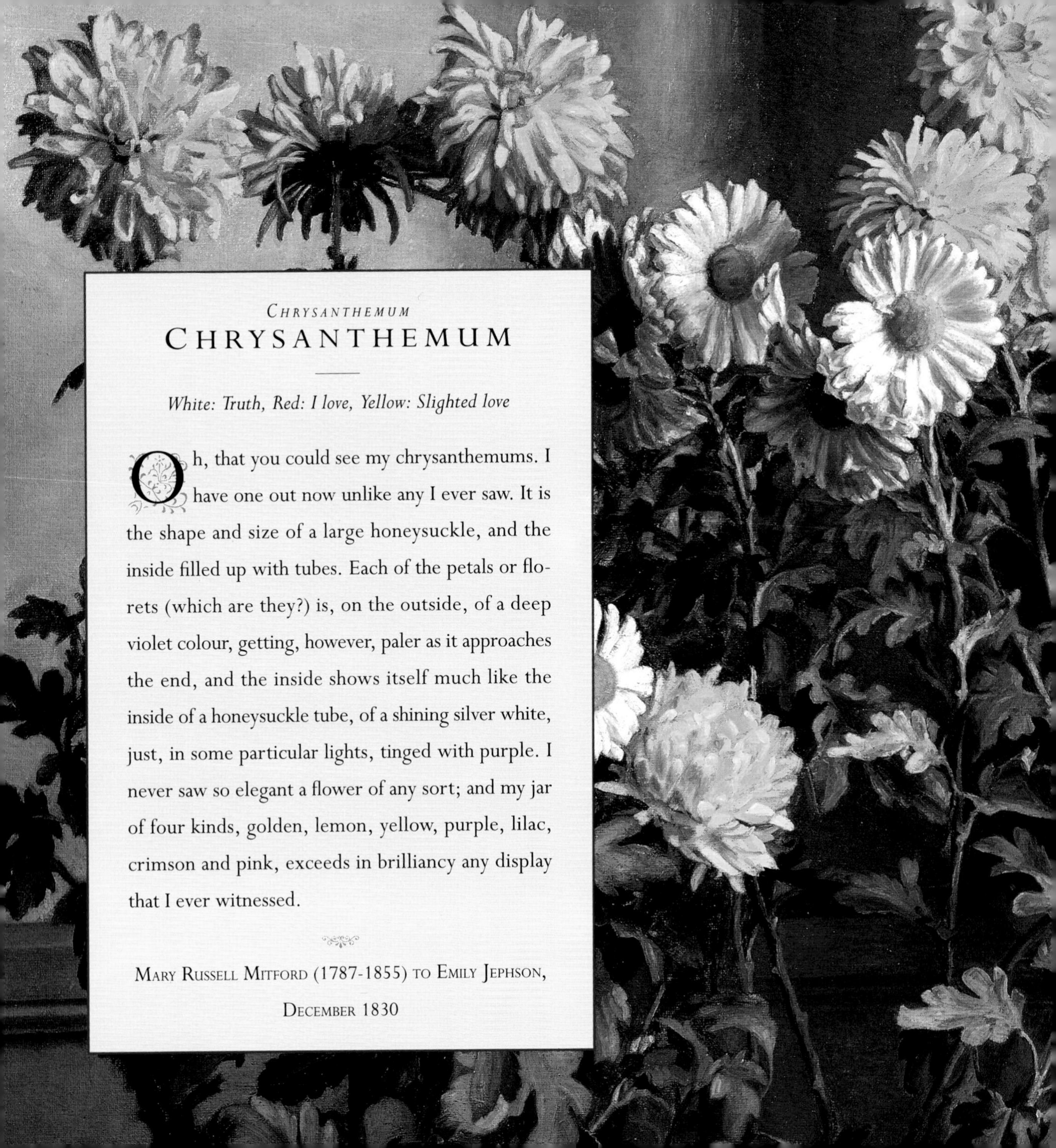

*Chrysanthemum*

# CHRYSANTHEMUM

*White: Truth, Red: I love, Yellow: Slighted love*

Oh, that you could see my chrysanthemums. I have one out now unlike any I ever saw. It is the shape and size of a large honeysuckle, and the inside filled up with tubes. Each of the petals or florets (which are they?) is, on the outside, of a deep violet colour, getting, however, paler as it approaches the end, and the inside shows itself much like the inside of a honeysuckle tube, of a shining silver white, just, in some particular lights, tinged with purple. I never saw so elegant a flower of any sort; and my jar of four kinds, golden, lemon, yellow, purple, lilac, crimson and pink, exceeds in brilliancy any display that I ever witnessed.

Mary Russell Mitford (1787-1855) to Emily Jephson, December 1830

*Cistus*

# Rock Rose

*Popular favour*

A better claim Sweet Cistus may pretend,
Whose sweating leaves a fragrant balsam send.
To crop the plant the wicked goat presumes,
Whose fetid beard the precious balm perfumes
But in revenge of the unhallow'd theft
The Caitiff's of his larded beard bereft,
Baldness thou dost redress, nor are we sure
Whether the beard or balsam gives the cure.

Abraham Cowley (1618-67)

Name ..............................
Address ..............................
..............................
..............................
Telephone ..............................

Name ..............................
Address ..............................
..............................
..............................
Telephone ..............................

Name ..............................
Address ..............................
..............................
..............................
Telephone ..............................

Name ..............................
Address ..............................
..............................
..............................
Telephone ..............................

Through the thick corn the scarlet poppies peep,
And round green roots and yellowing stalks I see
Pale pink convolvus in tendrils creep.

FROM *THE SCHOLAR GYPSY*
BY MATTHEW ARNOLD
(1822-1888)

Name ..............................
Address ..............................
..............................
..............................
Telephone ..............................

Name ..............................
Address ..............................
..............................
..............................
Telephone ..............................

Name ..............................
Address ..............................
..............................
..............................
Telephone ..............................

Name ..............................
Address ..............................
..............................
..............................
Telephone ..............................

Name ..............................
Address ..............................
..............................
..............................
Telephone ..............................

Name ..............................
Address ..............................
..............................
..............................
Telephone ..............................

# T and U

Name ..................................................
Address ..................................................
..................................................
..................................................
Telephone ..................................................

Name ..................................................
Address ..................................................
..................................................
..................................................
Telephone ..................................................

Name ..................................................
Address ..................................................
..................................................
..................................................
Telephone ..................................................

Name ..................................................
Address ..................................................
..................................................
..................................................
Telephone ..................................................

Name ..................................................
Address ..................................................
..................................................
..................................................
Telephone ..................................................

Name ..................................................
Address ..................................................
..................................................
..................................................
Telephone ..................................................

Name ..................................................
Address ..................................................
..................................................
..................................................
Telephone ..................................................

Name ..................................................
Address ..................................................
..................................................
..................................................
Telephone ..................................................

Name ..................................................
Address ..................................................
..................................................
..................................................
Telephone ..................................................

You violets that
first appeare,
By your pure purple
mantles known,
Like the proud virgins
of the yeare
As if the spring were
all your owne,
What are you when the
Rose is blown?

SIR HENRY WOTTON
(1568-1639)

The hard bitter feeling was getting pretty bad, when the maid brought in a box of flowers. Before she could speak, Annie had the cover off, and all were exclaiming at the lovely roses, heath, and ferns within.

"It's for Belle, of course; George always sends her some, but these are altogether ravishing," cried Annie, with a great sniff.

"They are for Miss March, the man said. And here's a note," put in the maid, holding it to Meg.

"What fun! Who are they from? Didn't know you had a lover," cried the girls, fluttering about Meg in a high state of curiosity and surprise.

"The note is from mother, and the flowers from Laurie," said Meg, simply, yet much gratified that he had not forgotten her.

"Oh indeed!" said Annie, with a funny look, as Meg slipped the note into her pocket, as a sort of talisman against envy, vanity, and false pride; for the few loving words had done her good, and the flowers cheered her up by their beauty.

FROM *LITTLE WOMEN* BY LOUISA MAY ALCOTT (1832–88)

# V

Name
Address

Telephone

Name
Address

Telephone

Name
Address

Telephone

I plucked pink blossoms
from mine apple-tree
And wore them all that
evening in my hair.

FROM *AN APPLE GATHERING*
BY CHRISTINA ROSSETTI
(1830-1894)

Name
Address

Telephone

Name
Address

Telephone

Name
Address

Telephone

Name
Address

Telephone

Name
Address

Telephone

Name
Address

Telephone

Name
Address

Telephone

Sound of vernal showers
On the twinkling grass,
Rain-awakened flowers,
All that ever was
Joyous and clear and fresh, thy music doth surpass.

FROM *TO A SKYLARK*
BY PERCY BYSSE SHELLEY
(1792-1822)

Name ..................
Address ..................
..................
..................
Telephone ..................

Name ..................
Address ..................
..................
..................
Telephone ..................

Name ..................
Address ..................
..................
..................
Telephone ..................

Name ..................
Address ..................
..................
..................
Telephone ..................

Name ..................
Address ..................
..................
..................
Telephone ..................

Name ..................
Address ..................
..................
..................
Telephone ..................

Name ..................
Address ..................
..................
..................
Telephone ..................

Name ..................
Address ..................
..................
..................
Telephone ..................

Name ..................
Address ..................
..................
..................
Telephone ..................

Name ..................
Address ..................
..................
..................
Telephone ..................

*Alcea*

# Hollyhock

*Ambition, Fecundity*

I am no Florist, at least not a Scientific one, but I have enough independence of mind to judge for myself without asking the self-named Connoisseurs when I must be pleased and when I must criticize what they are pleased to denounce as the inferior works of Nature. All have their characteristic beauties & in my parterre the humble Cowslip, or the unpretending Foxglove finds as hearty a welcome as the Crown Imperial or the stately and exuberant Holyoake.

FROM *MY HOUSE AND GARDEN* (1828) BY JAMES LUCKOCK

*Anemone*

# WINDFLOWER

*Forsaken*

The wood-anemonie through dead oak-leaves
And in the thickest wood now blooms anew
And where the green briar and the bramble weaves
Thick clumps o' green anemonies thicker grew
And weeping flowers in thousands pearled in dew
People the woods and brake's hid hollows there
White, yellow, and purple-hued the wide wood through
What pretty drooping weeping flowers they are.
The clipt frilled leaves the slender stalk they bear
On which the drooping flower hangs, weeping dew.

FROM *WOOD-ANEMONIE* BY JOHN CLARE (1793–1864)

Name

Address

Telephone

Name

Address

Telephone

Name

Address

Telephone

Name

Address

Telephone

Name

Address

Telephone

Name

Address

Telephone

Name

Address

Telephone

Name

Address

Telephone

Name

Address

Telephone

Name

Address

Telephone

Within the garden's
peaceful scene
Appear'd two lovely foes,
Aspiring to the rank
of queen –
The Lily and the Rose.

FROM *THE LILY AND THE ROSE*
BY WILLIAM COWPER
(1731-1800)

Name

Address

Telephone

Name
Address

Telephone

Name
Address

Telephone

Name
Address

Telephone

Name
Address

Telephone

Name
Address

Telephone

Name
Address

Telephone

Name
Address

Telephone

Name
Address

Telephone

Ladies fair I bring to you
Lavender with spikes of blue;
Sweeter plant was never found
Growing on an English ground.

FROM
*A BUNCH OF SWEET LAVENDER*
BY CONTANCE ISHERWOOD
(1900)

Name
Address

Telephone

# Acknowledgements

The Publishers thank the agencies below for permission to reproduce the following images:

Fine Art Photographic: p8–9 Thomas Ralph Spence, *The Sleeping Beauty*, Paisnel Gallery; p12 Christine Lovmand, *A Still Life of a Cactus, Lilies and Passion Flowers on a Windowsill*; p16 Johan Laurentz Jensen Rubrum, *Lilies and Fuchsias*, Verner Amell Limited; p17 John Atkinson Grimshaw, *Fair Maids in February*; p21 Eugene Henri Cauchois, *Springtime*, Stogell Gallery; p25 Oluf August Hermansen, *A Peony, Pinks and an Anemone*; p28 Madeleine Lemaire, *Peonies and Roses*, Baumkotter Gallery; p33 Ernest Rudolf Meyer, *A Study of Pink Roses and Butterflies*; p45 Daniel Sherrin, *The Bluebell Walk*, Private Collection; p48 Harry Watson, *Roses*, City Wall Gallery; p49 Rudolph Ernst, *The Perfume Maker*; p52 Harald Martin Hansen Holm, *Chrysanthemums*, Cambridge Fine Art; p56 Federigo Andreotti, *An Interesting Letter*, Burlington Paintings; p61 Maria Dorothea Krabbe, *Anemones and Forget-me-nots*, Philip Parker Esq..

Visual Arts Library, London: p2 Eugène Henri Cauchos, *Roses*; p13 Lais Hansen, *Primroses and Other Flowers*; p37 George Dionysius Ehret, *Manolia*; p41 Johan Laurentz Jensen, *A Bouquet of Roses*; p44 Paul Gauguin, *The Sunflowers*, Musée de l'Ermitage; p57 Auguste Renoir, *Still Life with Bouquet*, Houston Museum of Fine Art; p60 Thomas Sychkou, *Beside the Hollyhocks*.